**Bond**
*No.1 for exam success*

CW00400589

# English and **Verbal Reasoning**

## 10 Minute Tests

**CEM**
(Durham University)

## 8–9 years

OXFORD
UNIVERSITY PRESS

# Test 1: **Comprehension**

Read the text carefully and answer the questions that follow.

**School's Out!**

The children looked through the window with delight. They couldn't concentrate on what the teacher was saying and the clock ticked v–e–r–y s–l–o–w–l–y.

"Brrrrrnggggg!" The school bell eventually rang and every pupil sat upright in silence, looking carefully at the teacher. She smiled.                     5

"Well, children, as you are all sitting so beautifully, I think you can all put up your chairs and then let's get our coats on. Remember your gloves, scarves and hats and have you all got…"

Nobody heard the rest of the teacher's message. Coats, gloves, scarves, hats – there was no messing about this Friday afternoon.          10

It had only been snowing for the last hour, but it was enough to dust everywhere in the sweetest, prettiest, most magical icing sugar. It was a brilliant opportunity to make brand-new footsteps, to throw snowballs, to make snow angels and to build snowmen.

Feathery, fat flakes landed on their eyelashes and lips. This was          15
going to be a wonderful weekend.

**1**   Why couldn't the children concentrate?    `[1]`

_The teacher was talking very slow._

**2**   Why did the teacher smile at the children?    `[1]`

_Sitting nicely_

**3** What is the 'magical icing sugar' (line 12)?

It is snow

**4** Give **TWO** examples of things that the children could do in the snow.

throw snowballs

make snow angles!

**5** What effect do the dashes between the letters of 'v–e–r–y s–l–o–w–l–y' (line 3) have?

Trying to show you that is slow.

**6** How do you think the children will feel on Monday morning? Why do you think this?

Happy because on the weekend they got to play in snow.

What do these words mean as used in the text?

**7** delight (line 1)  exitment

**8** opportunity (line 13)  Good time / Great

Total 10

# Test 2: **Missing Words**

Read the following paragraph and add one word from the list to each space so that the paragraph makes sense. There are more words than there are spaces so some will be left out, but each word can only be used once.

| | | | | |
|---|---|---|---|---|
| bell | confident | glided | jumped | painted |
| scratched | steady | stretched | wet | whistle |

**1–6** Kim's hands shook slightly. She felt a bit sick, but with excitement rather

than fear. The swimming pool ___*stretched*___ ahead a very

long way. The official blew his ___*whistle*___ and the six

swimmers all ___*jumped*___ into the water. Although it wasn't

a race, Kim still wanted to do well. She shivered until her body adjusted

to the cool water. Kim kicked her feet up and down, her hands stretching

smoothly out as she ___*glided*___ through the water. "Turn

your head, keep a ___*steady*___ rhythm, breathe properly…"

Kim could remember everything that her coach had said. She turned and

felt ___*confident*___ now that she was on the homeward stretch

for a new swimming badge and certificate.

Find the three-letter word that is needed to complete each word so that each sentence makes sense. The missing three letters must make a word.

**Example:** The boy pedalled his b___*icy*___cle up the hill. (bicycle)

7   The tooth fairy had placed a coin under her pil___*low*___.

8   She placed the fragrant fl___*owe*___rs in the vase.

9   Our ___*tea*___cher is reading a book to us in school.

10   The dog was lying in front of the flaming _____eside.

The following sentences all have **ONE** word missing. Complete the sentences by selecting a word from options **a–e**.

11   Ben ___*borrowed*___several books from the library.

   **a** owed      **b** learned      **c** donated      **d** gave      **e** borrowed

12   Granny baked some cakes for the ___*party*___.

   **a** year      **b** breakfast      **c** eat      **d** party      **e** food

13   My hands were so ___*cold*___ that I put my gloves on.

   **a** pretty      **b** cold      **c** wet      **d** hot      **e** annoying

14   The ___*doctor*___ prescribed the medicine for my little brother.

   **a** teacher      **b** receptionist      **c** health      **d** doctor      **e** vet

1.55 left of timer

5

# Test 3: **Matching Words**

Select the **ONE** word on the right that has the most **SIMILAR** meaning to the word on the left. Underline the correct answer.

**6**

1  accidental    **a** deliberate   **b** purposeful   **c** aim   **d** unplanned   **e** shot

2  early    **a** premature   **b** late   **c** delay   **d** tardy   **e** hardy

3  knowledge    **a** school   **b** teach   **c** information   **d** learn   **e** lesson

4  question    **a** answer   **b** reply   **c** watch   **d** query   **e** ignore

5  actual    **a** real   **b** fake   **c** tasty   **d** wanted   **e** artificial

6  earth    **a** spoil   **b** soil   **c** stile   **d** tile   **e** life

Select the **ONE** word on the right that has the most **OPPOSITE** meaning to the word on the left. Underline the correct answer.

**7**

7  probable    **a** possible   **b** likely   **c** doubtful   **d** never   **e** always

8  difficult    **a** tricky   **b** complex   **c** similar   **d** simple   **e** sensible

9  often    **a** frequent   **b** rarely   **c** sometimes   **d** not   **e** ever

10  teacher    **a** trainer   **b** coach   **c** pupil   **d** lesson   **e** session

**11** women      **a** man    **b** boy   **c** men   **d** people   **e** adult

**12** strong      **a** powerful   **b** robust   **c** independent   **d** weak   **e** loss

**13** fresh      **a** unfashionable   **b** stale   **c** smart   **d** unhealthy   **e** roasted

Read the following sentences and answer the questions with the most sensible word.

'She could not bear to be too hot.'

**14** What does the word 'bear' mean as used in the sentence?

     **a** sit     **b** run     **c** stand     **d** find     **e** make

'He did not know why they had called a sudden meeting.'

**15** What does the word 'sudden' mean as used in the sentence?

     **a** booked     **b** unexpected     **c** important     **d** vital     **e** planned

'Tom was certain he had seen the man before.'

**16** What does the word 'certain' mean as used in the sentence?

     **a** shore     **b** unsure     **c** sure     **d** shire     **e** shy

'People in deckchairs lazed on the beach.'

**17** What does the word 'lazed' mean as used in the sentence?

     **a** slept     **b** ignored     **c** played     **d** relaxed     **e** sat

Total   17

# Test 4: **Mixed**

Read the text carefully and answer the questions that follow.

### Break-in at Antique Shop

At 14:35 on 12<sup>th</sup> June, police were called to the shop at the corner
of High Street and Farm Road after reports of a break-in. As it was
half-day closing, the owner, Mrs Harris, was away from the property.
Police surrounded the shop; however, the amount of noise heard
suggested that the culprit was still in the building. The police      5
entered the shop to find a stray cat had been let in and, in trying to
find an exit, the cat had knocked over many of the antiques for
sale in the shop. Mrs Harris was contacted and said, "The cat must
have entered the shop without me noticing and then moved in front
of the alarm beam. In a couple of hours, the cat has caused about      10
£120 000 worth of irreparable damage."

**1** Why had the police gone to the shop? Give **TWO** reasons.    `2`

_____

_____

**2** Why wasn't the shop owner at the shop?    `1`

_____

**3** How do you think Mrs Harris felt after the police contacted her? Use the
text to support your answer.    `2`

_____

_____

Find the three-letter word that is needed to complete each word so that each sentence makes sense. The missing three letters must make a word.

4

4  The car lurched for_____ds, narrowly missing the steep drop.

5  The pupils had been quietly wri_____g letters all morning.

6  The poster said 'Import_____ Warning: Slippery Floor'.

7  Although the weather wasn't dreadful, it had been s_____ting with rain.

Read the following sentences and answer the questions with the most sensible word.

3

'Can you remember the capital city of Latvia?'

8  What does the word 'remember' mean as used in the sentence?

   **a** visit    **b** revisit    **c** collect    **d** recollect    **e** find

'They were camping out and living on basic rations.'

9  What does the word 'basic' mean as used in the sentence?

   **a** essential    **b** elaborate    **c** tasty    **d** awful    **e** fancy

'The latest books are on the top shelf.'

10  What does the word 'latest' mean as used in the sentence?

   **a** best    **b** cheapest    **c** earliest    **d** last    **e** newest

Total        12

# Test 5: **Missing Letters**

Find the three-letter word that is needed to complete each word so that each sentence makes sense. The missing three letters must make a word.

**Example:** The boy pedalled his b___*icy*___cle up the hill. (bicycle)

4

**1** We had fun in the _____ chen when we iced cakes.

**2** We have a new shower in our _____ hroom.

**3** Darren's new bed is really com_____ table.

**4** Fluffy, the pet rab_____, has a large hutch.

Add the missing three letters to the word on the right to make a word with a **SIMILAR** meaning to the word on the left.

4

**Example:** silent     q_*uie* t     (quiet)

**5** tired          sl_____ y

**6** noise          s_____ d

**7** gap            op_____ ng

**8** yell           sh_____

Find the missing four letters that need to be added to these words so that the text makes sense. The four letters do not have to make a word.

**4**

**9-12** The procession of ants ma_____d up the garden path in a

perfectly or_____d line. How did they know what to do? How

did they know where to go? Studying them carefully, I saw that they were

ca_____ng fragments of leaf to a space between two paving

slabs and then, with one smooth movement, they disa_____red.

Who knows where they were going?

Add the missing four letters to the word on the right to make a word with an **OPPOSITE** meaning to the word on the left.

**6**

**Example:** noisy       s *ilen* t       (silent)

**13** rising                fa_____g

**14** calm                 ex_____d

**15** connected        iso_____d

**16** starting             fin_____ng

**17** contracting       expa_____g

**18** independent     accomp_____d

Total   18

# Test 6: **Missing Words**

Choose **ONE** word that is the best fit in each of these sentences. Underline your answer from the options **a–d**.

**4**

**1** The cyclist had to _____ hard to get up the hill.

   **a** walk    **b** drive    **c** paddle    **d** pedal

**2** The _____ was pleased to count so many new lambs.

   **a** gardener    **b** farmer    **c** policewoman    **d** fireman

**3** The calendar is divided into four _____.

   **a** chapters    **b** weeks    **c** seasons    **d** months

**4** Maurice played the piano for half an hour _____ day.

   **a** no    **b** some    **c** every    **d** all

Read the following paragraph and add one word from the list to each space so that the paragraph makes sense. Each word can only be used once.

**4**

| climbs | front | habit | world |
|---|---|---|---|

**5–8** Poppet, my rabbit, has a very funny _____ of tipping

her food bowl upside down. She then _____ on top

of her bowl and stamps her front right paw up and down before she

changes paws and stamps the _____ left paw up

and down. Dad says that Poppet is tap-dancing. Mum says that Poppet is

communicating with rabbits around the _____. I think

that Poppet is just a very funny rabbit.

Find the three-letter word that is needed to complete each word so
that each sentence makes sense. The missing three letters must make
a word. Underline one answer for each question.

**Example:** The boy pedalled his b_____cle up the hill.

**a** act    **b** <u>icy</u>    **c** lay    **d** air    **e** ice

9   My brother has a com_____er to help him with his homework.

    **a** but    **b** cut    **c** nut    **d** put    **e** rut

10  Tom is w_____ing a new football shirt.

    **a** are    **b** ear    **c** err    **d** ire    **e** our

11  In the dark sky, the moon _____med huge.

    **a** pea    **b** tea    **c** tee    **d** sea    **e** see

12  We take our dog for long walks in the _____est.

    **a** mar    **b** for    **c** pot    **d** tot    **e** war

13  She pa_____d to take a breath.

    **a** toe    **b** sue    **c** use    **d** woe    **e** our

14  He carried the s_____ping home in his bicycle basket.

    **a** hop    **b** hip    **c** lip    **d** lap    **e** cap

6

Total    14

# Test 7: **Matching Words**

Look at the words in the grid and then use them to answer the questions that follow.

8

| **a** appear | **b** medicine | **c** weep | **d** grammar | **e** ordinary |
| --- | --- | --- | --- | --- |
| **f** although | **g** enormous | **h** library | **i** believe | **j** round |
| **k** young | **l** potatoes | **m** huge | **n** bicycle | **o** usual |
| **p** therefore | **q** answer | **r** history | **s** immature | **t** square |
| **u** bawl | **v** porridge | **w** accept | **x** circle | **y** arrive |

1   Find **TWO** words that are **OPPOSITE** to the word 'old'.

_____        _____

2   Find **TWO** words that are **OPPOSITE** to the word 'small'.

_____        _____

3   Find **TWO** words that are most **SIMILAR** to the word 'cry'.

_____        _____

4   Find **TWO** words that are most **SIMILAR** to the word 'everyday'.

_____        _____

Read the following sentences and select the **ONE** word that answers the questions. Underline the correct answer.

4

'I was positive that the book was on the table.'

5   What does the word 'positive' mean as used in the sentence?

**a** certain      **b** sore      **c** afraid      **d** wondering      **e** unsure

'Dad increased the cost of bread in the shop.'

**6** What does the word 'increased' mean as used in the sentence?

**a** reduced     **b** improved     **c** raised     **d** checked     **e** decreased

'The courageous girl raised the alarm, then helped the lost child.'

**7** What does the word 'courageous' mean as used in the sentence?

**a** useful     **b** kind     **c** friendly     **d** helpful     **e** brave

'There were several shops in the location.'

**8** What does the word 'location' mean as used in the sentence?

**a** holiday     **b** village     **c** area     **d** building     **e** square

---

Select the **ONE** word on the right that has the most **SIMILAR** meaning to the word on the left. Underline the correct answer.

6

**9** decide          **a** choose     **b** side     **c** team     **d** ruler

**10** different          **a** dissimilar     **b** same     **c** identical     **d** alike

**11** material          **a** colour     **b** dress     **c** fabric     **d** wool

**12** strange          **a** double     **b** thread     **c** weak     **d** odd

**13** astonish          **a** expect     **b** amaze     **c** explain     **d** warn

**14** tremble          **a** tumble     **b** steady     **c** shake     **d** thump

Total     18

# Test 8: **Mixed**

Find the three-letter word that is needed to complete each word so that each sentence makes sense. The missing three letters must make a word. Underline the **TWO** answers needed from options **a–e**.

**1** We al _____ s use punctuation at the end of a sen _____ ce.

    **a** aye     **b** tan     **c** ten     **d** ton     **e** way

**2** A cal _____ ar is used to record d _____ s.

    **a** and     **b** are     **c** ate     **d** eat     **e** end

**3** An _____ a of land surrounded by water is called an isl _____ .

    **a** air     **b** and     **c** are     **d** try     **e** wry

**4** My fav _____ ite time of the year is the _____ mer.

    **a** are     **b** our     **c** out     **d** sum     **e** tum

**5** We love to eat homemade to _____ o soup with crou _____ s.

    **a** man     **b** mat     **c** mut     **d** ton     **e** tum

Choose **ONE** word that is the best fit in each of these sentences. Underline your answer from options **a–d**.

**5**

**6** The _____ monkey pinched all of the bananas.

    **a** natty     **b** naughtiness     **c** naughty     **d** nought

**7**  The second month of the year is _____.

    **a** April    **b** February    **c** January    **d** March

**8**  The teacher showed everyone a science _____.

    **a** art    **b** entertainment    **c** experiment    **d** mention

**9**  The mayor opened the new hospital _____.

    **a** bed    **b** cabin    **c** flight    **d** wing

**10**  Dad liked to drink coffee with _____ in it.

    **a** pepper    **b** sugar    **c** tea    **d** sweet

---

Find the missing three letters that complete these words. The three letters do not have to make a word. The same three letters are used for both words.

    5

**11**  h e i _____ e n            e i _____

**12**  r _____ m b e r            e x t r _____ l y

**13**  p a r t i _____ a r          p e _____ i a r

**14**  a c t _____ t y            c _____ l i s e

**15**  p h a _____ m             c o _____ u r

Total    20

# Test 9: **Comprehension**

Read the text carefully and then answer the questions that follow.

## Survival in the Snow

The engine suddenly cut out. There was complete silence for a few
seconds before the plane began to drop. Brin's heart thumped, his
hands felt hot and sticky; he felt sick and his head hurt. Carefully
scrambling to the side of the plane, he yanked at the door, but it didn't
budge. Then, using all of his strength, he tugged hard and eventually    **5**
it yielded. He looked around in panic, but time was running out. With
one last look, Brin edged forwards and just before the plane made
contact with the ground, he pushed himself out.

Brin landed heavily on his ankle, but the snow was deep and thick
so nothing else was injured and the icy coldness would prevent any    **10**
swelling. He tried to pull himself up, but it was too difficult to stand.
The plane had landed nose down with several parts broken off. Brin
found a side panel that could be used as a makeshift toboggan.
Sitting on top of it, he fastened his bag full of important documents
around his waist and around the side panel so that they were united    **15**
as one. He gently pushed the side panel along the snow and down
the mountainside. His mission might yet be a success.

**1** How had Brin reached the mountain? Underline the correct answer.    `1`

   **a** by helicopter      **b** by toboggan      **c** by train

   **d** by plane      **e** by car

**2** How did Brin get down the mountain? Underline the correct answer.    `1`

   **a** He climbed.      **b** He flew.      **c** He fell.

   **d** He limped.      **e** He slid.

**3** Why was it hard for Brin to stand up? Underline **TWO** answers.

2

   **a** His heart was thumping too quickly.

   **b** The snow was too deep to stand in.

   **c** He didn't want to be seen.

   **d** His ankle was too painful.

   **e** He was too scared from his ordeal.

**4** What do you think Brin's mission was? Underline the correct answer.

   **a** to hide the plane in the snow

   **b** to pass on some documents

   **c** to get to the mountain

   **d** to land the plane safely

   **e** to meet someone on the mountain

**5** How do you think Brin felt at the start of the text? Underline the correct answer.

   **a** scared        **b** excited        **c** happy

   **d** relaxed       **e** angry

**6** Which two-word phrase is used to mean 'it opened'? Underline the correct answer.

   **a** cut out        **b** it yielded      **c** running out

   **d** made contact   **e** nose down

**7** What does the word 'budge' (line 5) mean as used in the text? Underline the correct answer.

   **a** adapt         **b** resist        **c** move

   **d** quit          **e** stay

Total   8

# Test 10: **Missing Words**

 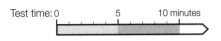

Read the following paragraph and add one word from the list to each space so that the paragraph makes sense. Each word can only be used once.

6

| Canada | firm | patch | rolled | wall | wooden |

**1–6** In some parts of _____ it is a winter tradition to make

maple syrup lollipops. Firstly, you need to find a flat surface, such as a

low _____ that has some freshly fallen snow on it.

This is important to make sure that the snow is clean. Pack down the

snow until it forms a _____ surface so that flakes of

loose snow don't stick on the lollipop. Next, you place the maple syrup

in a pan and heat it up on the stove until it reaches boiling point (ask an

adult to help – it will get very hot!). Now take the sticky syrup outside

and pour it onto the snow, where it will immediately begin to freeze.

A _____ lollipop stick can be pushed into

the _____ of syrup and then quickly

_____ up to make a lollipop before the syrup

becomes solid and brittle.

Find the three-letter word that is needed to complete each word so that each sentence makes sense. The missing three letters must make a word.

**Example:** The boy pedalled his b___*icy*___cle up the hill. (bicycle)

7  It was an acci_____t when the boy bumped into the shop display.

8  The cold air made it hard for me to br_____he.

9  It is really impor_____t to avoid looking directly at the sun.

10  You could p_____ably fit six cupcakes in this cake box.

11  There are sixty mi_____es in one hour.

The following sentences all have **ONE** word missing. Complete the sentences by selecting a word from options **a–e**.

12  The celebrity wrote an _____ that everyone wanted to read.

   **a** address     **b** autobiography     **c** antique     **d** actor     **e** act

13  It would be _____ to stand on one leg for five hours.

   **a** balance     **b** fun     **c** simple     **d** difficult     **e** easy

14  A school _____ is a group of children who sing together.

   **a** teacher     **b** class     **c** choir     **d** band     **e** orchestra

15  As there were four of us, Dad cut the pizza into _____.

   **a** halves     **b** quarters     **c** bits     **d** sixths     **e** centimetres

Total  15

# Test 11: **Missing Letters**

In each of the following words there are some letters missing. Complete each word by underlining the missing letters from options **a–e** to make a word that has an **OPPOSITE** meaning to the word on the left.

4

**Example:** start      f __ n __ s __ (finish)

     **a** i e s     **b** i s h     **c** e a t     **d** <u>i i h</u>     **e** a i t

**1**   escaped      c __ u __ h __

     **a** a g t     **b** o g t     **c** r s t     **d** h r s     **e** l s y

**2**   weak      __ t __ o __ g

     **a** s o n     **b** s h n     **c** s r n     **d** s h r     **e** s r i

**3**   backward      f __ r __ a __ d

     **a** a l n     **b** a w r     **c** u w r     **d** o w r     **e** o l n

**4**   bent      __ t __ a __ g __ t

     **a** s r y h     **b** s r y a     **c** s r i h     **d** s r i e     **e** s w i h

---

Find the missing three letters that complete these words. The three letters do not have to make a word. Underline the correct answer from options **a–e**.

6

**5**   disap _____ r

     **a** ear     **b** pea     **c** pee     **d** eer     **e** pie

**6**   busi _____ s

     **a** est     **b** nis     **c** nas     **d** nes     **e** les

**7** exper_____ce

    **a** ean    **b** ian    **c** ien    **d** een    **e** ese

**8** o_____sionally

    **a** cka    **b** cke    **c** cki    **d** cca    **e** cci

**9** posses_____n

    **a** sio    **b** sea    **c** see    **d** hio    **e** sho

**10** anti_____ckwise

    **a** coo    **b** clo    **c** cla    **d** clu    **e** cle

---

Find the missing three letters that complete these words. The three letters do not have to make a word. The same three letters are used for both words. Underline the correct answer from options **a–e**.

**11** mea_____e          in_____ance

    **a** sre    **b** use    **c** sur    **d** tre    **e** tru

**12** hol_____y          br_____l

    **a** dar    **b** iya    **c** ide    **d** adi    **e** ida

**13** t_____kful          merc_____t

    **a** ank    **b** han    **c** hun    **d** har    **e** aha

# Test 12: **Mixed**

Read the text carefully and answer the questions that follow.

**The Gingerbread House**

A crunchy path of brittle toffee

Leads past a tiny pool of coffee

And up to the gingerbread door.

Five chocolate teddy bears stand like little guards,

The window panes in red and green all made from sweet fruit shards.     **5**

Each wall has icing along the edges,

Under the windows are liquorice ledges.

The wintry roof is glazed with ice –

Our gingerbread house for sugar mice.

**1**   What are the teddy bears made of?       ☐ 1

_____

**2**   What do the fruit sweets make?       ☐ 1

_____

**3**   What lives in the gingerbread house?       ☐ 1

_____

**4**   What word in the poem rhymes with 'ledges'?       ☐ 1

_____

Find the three-letter word that is needed to complete each word so that each sentence makes sense. The missing three letters must make a word.

2

**5** We are having a general k_____ledge quiz in school next week.

    **a** new    **b** now    **c** net    **d** not    **e** nut

**6** It is not easy to desc_____e a piece of art.

    **a** rob    **b** rot    **c** rib    **d** rut    **e** our

Add the missing letters to the word on the right to make a word with an **OPPOSITE** meaning to the word on the left. Underline the correct answer from options **a–e**.

4

**7** easy    d __ f __ i __ u __ t

    **a** i i c s    **b** i f c s    **c** i f c s    **d** i f c l    **e** i f c r

**8** sadly    h __ p __ i __ y

    **a** a p t    **b** o p t    **c** i p t    **d** i p l    **e** a p l

**9** brave    c o __ a __ d l __

    **a** w r y    **b** w n y    **c** y w r    **d** r w e    **e** r e e

**10** ugly    b __ a __ t __ f __ l

    **a** u e i u    **b** i u e u    **c** e a i u    **d** e u i u    **e** u e u i

Total 10

# Test 13: **Comprehension**

Read the text carefully and answer the questions that follow.

## Rebounder

This year was going to be a rubbish one. Dad's new wife was allergic
to dogs and Mum had moved into a flat that wouldn't allow pets, so
Bounder had to go to a rescue centre. Mindy was outside when Mum
took Bounder for a walk and returned alone. Mindy was sad and cried
a lot. She missed Bounder. The elderly couple next door were also     **5**
moving house. Everyone seemed to be moving away.

A removal van appeared and new neighbours moved in. There were
three children and the youngest one, Jack, seemed to be the same
age as Mindy. Mindy smiled at him and he smiled back. Mindy felt a
bit happier as she might have a new friend. She shared some sweets     **10**
with Jack and told him all about the past few months. Jack had an
idea. This was not just a good idea, it was the best-ever idea …

Jack had already asked for a dog, and now that the family had settled
in, his mum and dad took the three children to the rescue centre to
find a dog. They all looked at big dogs, little dogs, friendly dogs, scary     **15**
dogs and then they found the perfect dog.

As soon as Bounder saw Mindy, he wagged his tail so hard that his
whole body shook. Mindy hugged him tightly, so excited to see her
dog again. She now had two best friends living next door and she
couldn't have been happier. This year was going to be the best ever!     **20**

**1**   Find **TWO** reasons why Bounder had to go to a rescue centre.     2

_____

_____

_____

**2** Why did Mindy feel a bit happier in paragraph two?

_____

**3** What do you think Jack's 'best-ever idea' (line 12) was?

_____

_____

**4** How had Mindy's feelings changed from the beginning of the text to the end of the text? Use the text to support your answer.

_____

_____

_____

_____

**5** In the last paragraph the word 'wag' has become 'wagged'. Find another word in the same paragraph that uses the same spelling rule.

_____

What do these phrases mean as used in the text?

**6** allergic to (lines 1–2) _____

**7** settled in (lines 13–14) _____

Total    9

# Test 14: **Matching Words**

Select the **ONE** word on the right that has the most **SIMILAR** meaning to the word on the left. Underline the correct answer.

**1** build     **a** create    **b** ruin    **c** free    **d** site    **e** glue

**2** group     **a** find    **b** mess    **c** set    **d** circle    **e** call

**3** thought     **a** think    **b** idea    **c** speak    **d** serious    **e** head

**4** centre     **a** around    **b** edge    **c** side    **d** shop    **e** middle

**5** perhaps     **a** happen    **b** sure    **c** no    **d** maybe    **e** yes

Read the following sentences and answer the questions with the most sensible word.

'Caz visited them quite often, but it was a surprise to see Andrew.'

**6** What does the word 'often' mean as used in the sentence?

   **a** frequently    **b** rarely    **c** rear    **d** over    **e** of

**7** What does the word 'surprise' mean as used in the sentence?

   **a** shock    **b** expected    **c** pleasure    **d** dislike    **e** dream

'Granny looked so glamorous when she attended the theatre.'

**8** What does the word 'glamorous' mean as used in the sentence?

   **a** pleased    **b** fun    **c** stylish    **d** shiny    **e** shabby

**9** What does the word 'attended' mean as used in the sentence?

    **a** right    **b** left    **c** departed    **d** avoided    **e** visited

'The fierce waves smashed against the harbour wall.'

**10** What does the word 'fierce' mean as used in the sentence?

    **a** vicious    **b** gentle    **c** unending    **d** weak    **e** wet

**11** What does the word 'smashed' mean as used in the sentence?

    **a** splintered    **b** smoothed    **c** reached    **d** tickled    **e** crashed

---

Select the **TWO** odd words out on each line. Select your answers by underlining **TWO** of the options **a–e**.

**Example: a** friend    **b** companion    **c** <u>compact</u>    **d** <u>converted</u>    **e** buddy

**12** **a** tall    **b** short    **c** low    **d** high    **e** towering

**13** **a** blue    **b** navy    **c** lemon    **d** orange    **e** lime

**14** **a** lamb    **b** calf    **c** foal    **d** donkey    **e** pig

**15** **a** sand    **b** glass    **c** soil    **d** brick    **e** plaster

**16** **a** wet    **b** damp    **c** dry    **d** moist    **e** parched

**17** **a** square    **b** rectangle    **c** round    **d** oval    **e** triangle

**18** **a** wide    **b** thin    **c** broad    **d** slim    **e** slender

Total    18

# Test 15: **Missing Words**

These sentences have been jumbled up and all have **ONE** extra word. Underline the word that is not needed.

**Example:** so cream <u>eat</u> the were cakes delicious

          (The cream cakes were so delicious.)

**1**   garden the in bathroom trees tall were there

**2**   the neck toes dipped we our into waves

**3**   bear teabag cuddled toddler her the fluffy

**4**   competition entering baking he was oven the

---

The following sentences all have **ONE** word missing. Complete the sentences by selecting a word from options **a–e**.

**5**  Mum _____ a long, pretty dress.

    **a** heard    **b** herd    **c** war    **d** wear    **e** wore

**6**  The dog _____ when the doorbell rang.

    **a** danced    **b** growled    **c** brayed    **d** cried    **e** flew

**7**  _____ yellow and red paint together makes orange paint.

    **a** Cooking    **b** Heating    **c** Eating    **d** Mixing    **e** Painting

**8** I am very _____ of my pet tortoise, Sybil.

    **a** kind    **b** find    **c** fond    **d** fine    **e** found

**9** The _____ of a hurricane is called the 'eye'.

    **a** circle    **b** name    **c** sight    **d** centre    **e** central

---

Read the following paragraph and add one word from the list to each space so that the paragraph makes sense. Each word can only be used once.

6

| bowl | dissolves | finally | set | thick | water |

**10–15** Marshmallows can be made by mixing cornflour and icing sugar together

in a _____ and sprinkling half of it in a baking tin.

Then add gelatine to a pan of _____ to soak for a

few minutes. Next, add sugar to a different pan and heat gently until

the sugar _____. Be careful, it will get very hot.

Using a whisk, mix the gelatine mixture with the syrup until it is very

_____. Pour the mixture into the baking sheet

and leave it to _____ for a few hours or overnight.

_____, cut into squares and roll each square in the

leftover cornflour and icing sugar mix.

Total    15

# Test 16: **Mixed**

Read the text carefully and answer the questions that follow.

## The Moon

The moon is easy to see in the night sky without needing a telescope. It waxes and wanes as it travels around Earth. When it waxes, the moon grows from a new moon until it becomes a full moon. When the moon wanes, it shrinks from a full moon back to a thin crescent moon. It takes 29 days for the moon to complete one cycle from a new moon back to the next new moon, and this is called a lunar month.

5

The moon is just over a quarter of the width of Earth and without the moon, life on Earth may not have been possible. The surface of the moon is covered in craters where large pieces of rock have hit it. It has no air to breathe and no life on it.

10

**1** Underline the **TWO** true statements.

2

    **a** Some of our months are longer than a lunar month.

    **b** It is called waxing when the moon appears to grow smaller.

    **c** The moon's surface is not smooth.

    **d** It is called waning when the moon appears to grow bigger.

    **e** The moon is larger than Earth.

**2** Underline the **TWO** false statements.

2

    **a** You need a telescope to see the moon.

    **b** The moon travels around Earth.

    **c** There is nothing growing on the moon.

    **d** Earth may not have had life without the moon.

    **e** The moon could not have life without Earth.

Select the **ONE** word on the right that has the most **SIMILAR** meaning to the word on the left. Underline the correct answer.

**3** numerous    **a** none    **b** many    **c** some    **d** all    **e** with

**4** weight    **a** mass    **b** light    **c** heavy    **d** scales    **e** fat

**5** strength    **a** length    **b** width    **c** breadth    **d** power    **e** cubed

---

Select the **TWO** odd words out on each line. Select your answers by underlining **TWO** of the options **a–e**.

**6**   **a** blanket    **b** sheet    **c** shower    **d** basin    **e** pillow

**7**   **a** cake    **b** bread    **c** coffee    **d** milk    **e** tea

**8**   **a** rose    **b** daisy    **c** tree    **d** shrub    **e** tulip

---

These sentences have been jumbled up and all have **ONE** extra word. Underline the word that is not needed.

**9**   church hill the upon the stood carrot

**10**   violin day brother played each Juliet her

**11**   the dog danced her tutu in ballerina

Total    13

# Test 17: **Missing Letters**

In each of the following words there are some letters missing. Complete each word by selecting the missing letters from options **a–e** to make a word that has an **OPPOSITE** meaning to the word on the left.

**4**

**Example:** start      f __ n __ s __ (finish)

**a** i e s     **b** i s h     **c** e a t     **d** i i h     **e** a i t

1   unknown         f __ m __ u __

    **a** i o r     **b** o o r     **c** e l r     **d** a o s     **e** a i s

2   unfinished      __ o __ p __ e __ e

    **a** c m l t     **b** c m r r     **c** c m r t     **d** c m l r     **e** c m t t

3   men            __ o __ e __

    **a** b w r     **b** l w r     **c** w m n     **d** w m r     **e** t r n

4   ill            h __ a __ t __ y

    **a** e l t     **b** e r t     **c** e l h     **d** e l e     **e** e l r

---

Find the missing four letters that need to be added to these words so that the sentence makes sense. The four letters do not have to make a word.

**6**

**Example:** I have great r_____m so I love to dance.

**a** ithe     **b** itit     **c** hyth     **d** hith     **e** itth

5   They liked to eat healthily and to e_____ise each day.

    **a** xers     **b** kser     **c** xirs     **d** ksir     **e** xerc

**6** Kim and Ben were mus_____ns and played lots of instruments.

    **a** icio    **b** icia    **c** isio    **d** isia    **e** isha

**7** The holiday b_____ure had lots of tempting holidays.

    **a** rows    **b** rous    **c** roch    **d** roww    **e** raws

**8** We had a gar_____r to cut the lawn and prune the flowers.

    **a** denn    **b** dane    **c** dnee    **d** rgen    **e** dene

**9** The as_____aut had to train a long time for his space mission.

    **a** tran    **b** torn    **c** trin    **d** tron    **e** tern

**10** Sharks have an ex_____ent sense of smell.

    **a** cele    **b** sell    **c** cill    **d** sill    **e** cell

---

Find the missing three letters that complete these words. The three letters do not have to make a word. The same three letters are used for both words.    ( 5

**11** c h a_____t e r        i n t e_____t i o n

**12** s u_____m a r k e t        i m_____f e c t l y

**13** t e l e v_____o n        d e c_____o n

**14** p r_____i c e        e x_____l y

**15** v e g_____b l e        t i m_____b l e

Total    15

# Test 18: **Comprehension**

Read the text carefully and answer the questions that follow.

### The Suitcase

Jim pushed open the bedroom door and tiptoed in. Nobody
had been here for years. There was dust in the air and the room
smelled old and musty. Heavy curtains hung at the window and
although they were mostly open, the miserable day meant there
was little light. He walked to the bed when a sound on the wooden    **5**
floorboard made him look down. It looked like he had kicked an old
metal bottle top. Jim bent down and, as he did so, his eyes drifted
to under the bed. There was a large suitcase under the bed and
something made Jim feel very curious.

He knelt on the floor and looked at the suitcase. It was black, old    **10**
and dusty and something about it worried Jim, although he wasn't
sure why. Jim touched it. The leather felt cold but soft. He pulled the
suitcase towards him. It felt so heavy. The suitcase had a dull, metal
lock on it with a small key hanging from a thread already in the lock.
Jim turned the key. It clicked open. Jim's hands and head felt hot, and    **15**
his heart was racing. He gripped the lid with both hands and very
slowly opened the suitcase. As he did so, a look of pure shock formed
on his face. Jim took in the contents of the suitcase. It was full of
money. Bags of coins, bundles of notes – not modern money, but old
money like Jim had seen on television programmes. Suddenly, there    **20**
was a sound downstairs. Jim swallowed hard. He was not alone …

**1**   What made Jim look under the bed?        1

_____

_____

*Test continues after Answers section →*

# Answers

## Test 1: Comprehension

1. The children could not concentrate because it was snowing outside (and/or they were anxious to go out to play in the snow).

2. The teacher smiled at the children because they were so well-behaved and sitting beautifully (and/or she knew that they were anxious to get out to play in the snow).

3. The 'magical icing sugar' is the freshly fallen snow.

4. 1 mark each for any two of the following points: make brand-new footsteps in the snow; throw snowballs; make snow angels; build snowmen.

5. It emphasises the slowness of time.

6. 1 mark each for how the children would feel and a reason why: the children would feel happy as they had played in the snow all weekend; they would feel disappointed because they have had to come back to school instead of playing; they would feel tired as they have spent all weekend playing out in the snow; they would feel excited because they wanted to tell their friends about their weekend.

7. 'Delight' means pleasure or happiness.

8. 'Opportunity' means a chance.

## Test 2: Missing Words

1. stretched
2. whistle
3. jumped
4. glided
5. steady
6. confident
7. low
8. owe
9. tea
10. fir
11. **e** borrowed
12. **d** party
13. **b** cold
14. **d** doctor

## Test 3: Matching Words

1. **d** unplanned
2. **a** premature
3. **c** information
4. **d** query
5. **a** real
6. **b** soil
7. **c** doubtful
8. **d** simple
9. **b** rarely
10. **c** pupil
11. **c** men
12. **d** weak
13. **b** stale
14. **c** stand
15. **b** unexpected
16. **c** sure
17. **d** relaxed

## Test 4: Mixed

1. The police had gone to the shop as there had been a report of a break-in (1 mark) and the alarm bell would have been ringing as the cat stepped in front of the alarm beam (1 mark).

2. It was half-day closing so the owner was not at the shop.

3. 1 mark for Mrs Harris would feel sad or upset and 1 mark for either of the following: the text says that 'the cat has caused about £120000 worth of irreparable damage'; the damage is 'irreparable', meaning that the items damaged can never be replaced or put right.

4. war
5. tin
6. ant
7. pit/pot
8. **d** recollect
9. **a** essential
10. **e** newest

## Test 5: Missing Letters

1. kit
2. bat
3. for

**4** bit

**5** eep (sleepy)

**6** oun (sound)

**7** eni (opening)

**8** out (shout)

**9** rche (marched)

**10** dere (ordered)

**11** rryi (carrying)

**12** ppea (disappear)

**13** llin (falling)

**14** cite (excited)

**15** late (isolated)

**16** ishi (finishing)

**17** ndin (expanding)

**18** anie (accompanied)

## Test 6: Missing Words

**1 d** pedal

**2 b** farmer

**3 c** seasons

**4 c** every

**5** habit

**6** climbs

**7** front

**8** world

**9 d** put

**10 b** ear

**11 e** see

**12 b** for

**13 c** use

**14 a** hop

## Test 7: Matching Words

**1 k** young, **s** immature

**2 g** enormous, **m** huge

**3 c** weep, **u** bawl

**4 e** ordinary, **o** usual

**5 a** certain

**6 c** raised

**7 e** brave

**8 c** area

**9 a** choose

**10 a** dissimilar

**11 c** fabric

**12 d** odd

**13 b** amaze

**14 c** shake

## Test 8: Mixed

**1 e, c** (We always use a full stop at the end of a sentence.)

**2 e, c** (A calendar is used to record dates.)

**3 c, b** (An area of land surrounded by water is called an island.)

**4 b, d** (My favourite time of year is the summer.)

**5 b, d** (We love to eat homemade tomato soup with croutons.)

**6 c** naughty

**7 b** February

**8 c** experiment

**9 d** wing

**10 b** sugar

**11** ght (heighten, eight)

**12** eme (remember, extremely)

**13** cul (particular, peculiar)

**14** ivi (activity, civilise)

**15** nto (phantom, contour)

## Test 9: Comprehension

**1 d** The text describes a plane crashing on the mountain.

**2 e** Brin used a side panel to make a toboggan to slide down the mountainside.

**3 b** The snow is described as 'deep and thick'.

   **d** Brin had hurt his ankle.

**4 b** The text states that Brin had a 'bag full of important documents'.

**5 a** Brin's heart thumped, his hands were hot and sticky, he felt sick and had a headache, which are all symptoms of being scared.

**6 b** When Brin tugged hard at the plane door 'it yielded', which means 'it opened'.

**7 c** Brin was trying to open the door, but it wouldn't budge, which means it wouldn't open.

## Test 10: Missing Words

| | | | |
|---|---|---|---|
| **1** | Canada | **9** | tan |
| **2** | wall | **10** | rob |
| **3** | firm | **11** | nut |
| **4** | wooden | **12 b** | autobiography |
| **5** | patch | **13 d** | difficult |
| **6** | rolled | **14 c** | choir |
| **7** | den | **15 b** | quarters |
| **8** | eat | | |

## Test 11: Missing Letters

**1 a** a g t (caught)

**2 c** s r n (strong)

**3 d** o w r (forward)

**4 c** s r i h (straight)

**5 b** pea (disappear)

**6 d** nes (business)

**7 c** ien (experience)

**8 d** cca (occasionally)

**9 a** sio (possession)

**10 b** clo (anticlockwise)

**11 c** sur (measure, insurance)

**12 e** ida (holiday, bridal)

**13 b** han (thankful, merchant)

## Test 12: Mixed

**1** The teddy bears are made of chocolate (line 4).

**2** The fruit sweets are used to make window panes (line 5).

**3** Sugar mice live in the gingerbread house (line 9).

**4** 'Edges' rhymes with 'ledges' (line 6).

**5 b** now

**6 c** rib

**7 d** i f c l (difficult)

**8 e** a p l (happily)

**9 a** w r y (cowardly)

**10 d** e u i u (beautiful)

## Test 13: Comprehension

**1** Dad's new wife was allergic to dogs (1 mark) and Mum's flat wouldn't allow pets (1 mark).

**2** Mindy felt a bit happier as she might have a new friend.

**3** Jack's 'best-ever idea' was to have Bounder as his family dog.

**4** 1 mark for either of the following: at the beginning Mindy thought that it was going to be a rubbish year because everyone was moving away; she was upset at having to send Bounder to a rescue centre. 1 mark for either of the following: at the end of the text she was happy to have her dog back; she was happy that she had made a new friend.

**5** 'Hugged' uses the same spelling rule as 'wagged'.

**6** 'Allergic to' means having a bad reaction to something.

**7** 'Settled in' means having got used to a new situation.

## Test 14: Matching Words

| | | | |
|---|---|---|---|
| **1 a** | create | **3 b** | idea |
| **2 c** | set | **4 e** | middle |

**5 d** maybe     **12 b** short, **c** low

**6 a** frequently     **13 a** blue, **b** navy

**7 a** shock     **14 d** donkey, **e** pig

**8 c** stylish     **15 a** sand, **c** soil

**9 e** visited     **16 c** dry, **e** parched

**10 a** vicious     **17 c** round, **d** oval

**11 e** crashed     **18 a** wide, **c** broad

## Test 15: Missing Words

**1** bathroom (There were tall trees in the garden. / In the garden there were tall trees.)

**2** neck (We dipped our toes into the waves.)

**3** teabag (The toddler cuddled her fluffy bear.)

**4** oven (He was entering the baking competition.)

**5 e** wore

**6 b** growled     **11** water

**7 d** Mixing     **12** dissolves

**8 c** fond     **13** thick

**9 d** centre     **14** set

**10** bowl     **15** Finally

## Test 16: Mixed

**1 a** The text states that a lunar month is 29 days long.

   **c** It states that the surface of the moon is covered in craters.

**2 a** It states that the moon is easy to see without a telescope.

   **e** It states that the moon has no life on it.

**3 b** many

**4 a** mass

**5 d** power

**6 c** shower, **d** basin

**7 a** cake, **b** bread

**8 c** tree, **d** shrub

**9** carrot (The church stood on the hill.)

**10** brother (Juliet played her violin each day. / Each day Juliet played her violin.)

**11** dog (The ballerina danced in her tutu.)

## Test 17: Missing Letters

**1 d** a o s (famous)

**2 a** c m l t (complete)

**3 c** w m n (women)

**4 c** e l h (healthy)

**5 e** xerc (exercise)

**6 b** icia (musicians)

**7 c** roch (brochure)

**8 e** dene (gardener)

**9 d** tron (astronaut)

**10 e** cell (excellent)

**11** rac (character, interaction)

**12** per (supermarket, imperfectly)

**13** isi (television, decision)

**14** act (practice, exactly)

**15** eta (vegetable, timetable)

## Test 18: Comprehension

**1** A sound from an old metal bottle top on the wooden floorboard made Jim look under the bed.

**2** Jim felt worried or scared (1 mark) because he realised that he was not alone in the house (1 mark).

**3** 1 mark each for any four of the following words: large, black, old, dusty, cold, soft, leather, heavy, full.

**4** Jim felt scared or nervous before opening the suitcase (1 mark) as the text says 'Jim's hands and head felt hot and his heart was racing' (1 mark).

**5** 1 mark each for any of the following four answers: there were bags of coins; there were bundles of notes; the money was not modern; the money was old like Jim had seen on television programmes.

## Test 19: Missing Words

**1** for
**2** net
**3** ode
**4** kin
**5** unrest
**6** difficult
**7** nature
**8** plant
**9** survive
**10** land
**11 c** address
**12 e** popular
**13 a** possible
**14 e** quay

## Test 20: Mixed

**1 d** p c a (special)
**2 d** o p s t (opposite)
**3 c** i o e (disobey)
**4** wife
**5** factory
**6** house
**7** artists
**8** open
**9** visitors
**10 e** ique (antique)
**11 b** cide (decided)
**12 d** agin (imagination)
**13 a** atch (watching)
**14 c** tcar (postcard)

## Test 21: Matching Words

**1 d** force
**2 a** leader
**3 c** governed
**4 d** early
**5 c** question

**6 d** starting
**7 b** regular, **s** frequent
**8 d** noise, **o** sound
**9 h** polite, **w** courteous
**10 t** circle, **y** ring
**11 j** picture, **m** imagine
**12 k** enough, **x** sufficient

## Test 22: Comprehension

**1** In step 4 it says to roll three parts together to make the body.

**2** The 'top tip' says that you can add more flour and salt if the dough is too wet.

**3** A hot oven can be dangerous so a responsible adult is needed for this stage.

**4** The purpose of baking the snowman is to dry him out. (The text makes it makes it clear that you don't have to use an oven as you can also allow the snowman to air-dry.)

**5** in = preposition

**6** head = noun

**7** and = conjunction

**8** blue = adjective

**9** mix = verb

## Test 23: Missing Words

**1 c** elephant (The ewe had given birth to a tiny lamb.)

**2 d** combined (There are many forests in the United Kingdom. / In the United Kingdom there are many forests.)

**3 e** feet (We always wash our hands before we prepare food. / Before we prepare food, we always wash our hands.)

**4 a** painted (Barry wrote a letter to the local newspaper.)

**5 c** monstrous, **e** ugly

6 **c** sea, **d** water

7 **d** carrots, **e** potato

8 **a** nose, **b** eyes

9 **b** invited

10 **c** found

11 **e** ice

12 **d** saucepan

13 **a** watch

14 **c** house

## Test 24: Mixed

1 **b** o e e t (movement)

2 **d** c l i i n (collision)

3 **c** r a u e (creature)

4 **c** flames

5 **b** rain

6 **a** frogs

7 **c** bread, **d** pasta

8 **b** rabbit, **d** dog

9 **c** holiday, **e** vacation

10 **c** aeroplane, **e** helicopter

11 **b** right

12 **c** over

13 **d** join

14 **c** noise

15 **a** fall

## Test 25: Matching Words

1 **b** protect

2 **e** nervous

3 **d** closed

4 **e** disappeared

5 **c** share

6 **d** upset

7 **b** see

8 **o** above, **t** over

9 **j** present, **x** here

10 **a** plain, **h** simple

11 **i** gently, **n** softly

12 **s** bury, **y** cover

13 **b** piece, **c** part

## Test 26: Comprehension

1 **a** The text states that 'if he found a spider, he would throw it at the person most scared of spiders'.

 **b** It states that 'if anyone had food, they would have to give it to Tom'.

 **d** Tom dares some of the boys to scare the dinner staff.

2 **d** The text states that 'his hair and his skin stank'.

3 **a** The text states that 'Tom very soon realised that it was horrible being laughed at'.

4 hair = noun

5 pointed = verb

6 but = conjunction

7 cold = adjective

8 he = pronoun

## Test 27: Missing Letters

1 **e** sono (poisonous)

2 **a** ryon (everyone)

3 **c** easu (treasure)

4 **c** ssib (impossible)

5 **c** e t o (mention)

6 **e** q e t o (question)

7 **c** o s d r (consider)

8 **d** o r c (correct)

9 **b** all (basically)

10 **e** sag (disagreeing)

**11 a** her (whether)

**12 d** use (museum)

## Test 28: Mixed

**1 d** award

**2 a** plan

**3 e** cost

**4 e** apples (We had vegetable curry with our rice. / We had rice with our vegetable curry.)

**5 c** bricks (The wind blew the leaves off the tree.)

**6 d** stems (Mum placed the scented roses in a vase.)

**7 b** bird (The goose waddled by with her little goslings.)

**8 b** camel, **d** elephant

**9 a** garage, **b** shed

**10 a** gallop, **d** skip

**11 b** marched

**12 e** nibbling

**13 d** theatre

**14 c** baked

## Test 29: Mixed

**1 b** kind, **f** type

**2 h** dull, **i** cloudy

**3 m** title, **r** name

**4 g** fresh, **u** new

**5 a** hot, **w** heated

**6 e** old, **n** aged

**7** born

**8** writer

**9** newspapers

**10** adults

**11** powerful

**12 c** awake

**13 e** full

**14 a** cold

**15 e** scruffy

## Test 30: Mixed

**1 c** ate (related)

**2 a** pat (impatient)

**3 e** war (afterwards)

**4 d** ace (peaceful)

**5 b** low (flowerpot)

**6 b** sad, **e** miserable

**7 a** hair, **c** skin

**8 c** pencil, **e** pen

**9 b** swimming, **d** cycling

**10 b** holiday, **e** weekend

**11 a** fog

**12 b** television

**13 d** submarine

**14 b** incorrect

**15 b** across

## Test 31: Mixed

**1 p** mean, **v** unkind

**2 e** fair, **s** light

**3 a** main, **g** key

**4 k** mail, **x** post

**5 l** soar, **t** fly

**6 b** chap, **u** man

**7 c** osit (position)

**8 a** tion (injections)

**9 e** noug (enough)

**10** board (I joined the school chess club.)

**11** colour (Scarlet is a shade of red.)

**12** hippopotamus (At the farm we milked a goat. / We milked a goat at the farm.)

# PUZZLE ANSWERS

## Puzzle 1

**Animals with 3-letter names:** pig, cow, cat, fox, hen, rat

**Animals with 4-letter names:** goat, fish, hare, bear, deer, lion

## Puzzle 2

Many different answers are possible. Here are a few examples:

**cat –** tiger – rabbit – terrapin – nightingale – elephant – tapir

**gorilla –** ape – elephant – tiger – rattlesnake – earwig – gnu

**walrus –** seal – llama – armadillo – owl – lion – newt

## Puzzle 3

**The drinks in order:** lemonade, tea, juice, milk, water

## Puzzle 4

**The fruits in order:** damson, plum, raspberry, cherry, apple, orange, grape, banana, lemon, mango, melon, lime, kiwi, grapefruit, pineapple, strawberry, peach, pear

## Puzzle 5

## Puzzle 6

| | | |
|---|---|---|
| 1 carrot | 8 sprouts | 15 chard |
| 2 parsnip | 9 beans | 16 leek |
| 3 cabbage | 10 peas | 17 celery |
| 4 cauliflower | 11 sweetcorn | 18 beetroot |
| 5 spinach | 12 kale | 19 courgette |
| 6 broccoli | 13 onion | 20 sweet |
| 7 potato | 14 turnip | potato |

## Puzzle 7

| | | | | |
|---|---|---|---|---|
| e | a | s | y | ■ |
| s | l | o | w | |
| p | u | p | i | l |
| e | n | d | ■ | |
| c | h | e | a | p |
| i | c | y | ■ | |
| a | w | a | k | e |
| l | a | s | t | ■ |
| l | a | r | g | e |
| y | e | l | l | ■ |

**Hidden word:** especially

## Puzzle 8

| | |
|---|---|
| 1 to/too | 7 so/sow |
| 2 for/fore | 8 where/ware |
| 3 story | 9 dear |
| 4 here | 10 knows |
| 5 fair/fayre | 11 pair/pare |
| 6 ewe/you | 12 weak |

**2**   How do you think Jim felt at the end of the text and why?
Use the text to support your answer.                                                    2

_____

_____

_____

**3**   Find **FOUR** words that are used to describe the old suitcase.                 4

_____          _____

_____          _____

**4**   How do you think Jim felt just before he opened the suitcase?
What words in the text make you think this?                                             2

_____

_____

_____

**5**   How does the text describe what was in the suitcase?
Find **FOUR** examples.                                                                4

_____

_____

_____

_____

Total    13

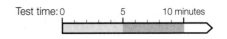

# Test 19: **Missing Words**

Find the three-letter word that is needed to complete each word so that each sentence makes sense. The missing three letters must make a word.

**Example:** The boy pedalled his b _____ *icy* _____ cle up the hill. (bicycle)

**1** The teacher gave us lots of in _____ mation about the night sky.

**2** She told us about pla _____ s such as Mars and Mercury.

**3** She explained how some stars expl _____ d with a last burst of energy.

**4** We are now buying a telescope for loo _____ g at the stars.

Read the following paragraph and add one word from the list to each space so that the paragraph makes sense. Each word can only be used once.

| difficult | land | nature | plant | survive | unrest |

**5–10** In 1649 there was great _____ in England. Food

prices were high and taxes made life very _____

for the poorest people in society. A group of people called 'The

Diggers' understood a deep relationship between people and

_____ and felt that Earth should be able

to feed the people who lived on it. They encouraged other people to

_____ fruit and vegetables on common land so that

even the very poor could afford to eat and to _____.

Although the Diggers offered no harm, many were beaten and

attacked by the landowners who wanted to drive the poor people

off their _____.

---

Choose **ONE** word that is the best fit in each of these sentences.
Underline your answer from options **a–e**.

4

**11** When we moved house we had a new _____.

    **a** dress    **b** add    **c** address    **d** addressing    **e** dressing

**12** This game is really _____ as all of my friends play it.

    **a** enough    **b** real    **c** rare    **d** unpopular    **e** popular

**13** Is it _____ to catch the last train home?

    **a** possible    **b** probable    **c** promise    **d** position    **e** purpose

**14** Trevor moored his fishing trawler alongside the _____.

    **a** holiday    **b** coast    **c** waves    **d** sea    **e** quay

Total    14

# Test 20: **Mixed**

In each of the following words there are some letters missing. Complete each word by selecting the missing letters from the options **a–e** to make a word that has an **OPPOSITE** meaning to the word on the left.

**1** ordinary        s __ e __ i __ l

   **a** p s a     **b** p s e     **c** p c o     **d** p c a     **e** p c e

**2** similar         __ p __ o __ i __ e

   **a** a p t s    **b** o p t s    **c** a p s t    **d** o p s t    **e** u p s t

**3** obey           d __ s __ b __ y

   **a** a o e     **b** u o e     **c** i o e     **d** e o e     **e** o o e

---

Read the following paragraph and add one word from the list to each space so that the paragraph makes sense. Each word can only be used once.

> artists      factory      house      open      visitors      wife

**4–9** Lord Leverhulme had an art gallery built for his _____.

It is in Port Sunlight, the village that he had built for the workers in

his _____. In the gallery are paintings, furniture,

ceramics and sculptures which are displayed together to recreate the

interior of a large _____. There are many famous

_____ represented and it is an interesting place to

look around. The art gallery is free to visit and is _____

every day. There is free parking right outside the door and there is a café

and shop for _____ to enjoy.

---

Find the missing four letters that need to be added to these words so that the sentence makes sense. The four letters do not have to make a word.

⬭ 5

**10** The ant_____ shop had so many old things in it.

    **a** eack    **b** eeck    **c** icke    **d** ikke    **e** ique

**11** Lewis de_____d to have his bedroom painted silver.

    **a** side    **b** cide    **c** syde    **d** cyed    **e** scid

**12** I like to write as I have a vivid im_____ation.

    **a** ajin    **b** ajen    **c** ajan    **d** agin    **e** agen

**13** We are w_____ing this new series on television.

    **a** atch    **b** ache    **c** atth    **d** acht    **e** otch

**14** Sally bought a pos_____d in the souvenir shop.

    **a** star    **b** trad    **c** tcar    **d** trac    **e** scat

Total | 14

# Test 21: **Matching Words**

Read the following sentences and answer the questions with the most sensible word.

'The fireman had to apply a lot of pressure to break the window.'

**1**   What does the word 'pressure' mean as used in the sentence?

   **a** length      **b** width      **c** volume      **d** force      **e** gravity

'We followed the guide as she took us to the town centre.'

**2**   What does the word 'guide' mean as used in the sentence?

   **a** leader      **b** brownie      **c** control      **d** torch      **e** teacher

'King William IV reigned for seven years.'

**3**   What does the word 'reigned' mean as used in the sentence?

   **a** lived      **b** died      **c** governed      **d** travelled      **e** reformed

Select the **ONE** word on the right that has the most **OPPOSITE** meaning to the word on the left. Underline the correct answer.

**4**   late      **a** annoy      **b** miss      **c** past      **d** early      **e** after

**5**   answer   **a** reply      **b** response      **c** question      **d** understand      **e** go

**6**   ending   **a** first      **b** finishing      **c** new      **d** starting      **e** over

Look at the words in the grid and then use them to answer the questions that follow.

| a length | b regular | c promise | d noise | e fail |
|---|---|---|---|---|
| f heart | g mention | h polite | i teach | j picture |
| k enough | l learn | m imagine | n refer | o sound |
| p consider | q heard | r through | s frequent | t circle |
| u breath | v fruit | w courteous | x sufficient | y ring |

7   Find **TWO** words that are **OPPOSITE** to the word 'uncommon'.

_____          _____

8   Find **TWO** words that are **OPPOSITE** to the word 'silence'.

_____          _____

9   Find **TWO** words that are **OPPOSITE** to the word 'rude'.

_____          _____

10   Find **TWO** words that are most **SIMILAR** to the word 'loop'.

_____          _____

11   Find **TWO** words that are most **SIMILAR** to the word 'see'.

_____          _____

12   Find **TWO** words that are most **SIMILAR** to the word 'adequate'.

_____          _____

Total     18

# Test 22: **Comprehension**

Read the text carefully and answer the questions that follow.

### Salt Dough Snowman

| Ingredients | Items needed |
|---|---|
| 3 tablespoons of salt | bowl to mix the dough in |
| 6 tablespoons of flour | paint |
| water | varnish (optional) |

**1** Mix the salt and the flour and then add water, a bit at a time, until you have a thick dough.                                                                                              5

**2** Knead the dough until it is smooth and soft.

**3** Divide the dough into 5 equal parts.

**4** Take 3 parts and roll them together to make an oval body.

**5** Take 1 part and roll it into a circle to make a head.                                                   10

**6** Use the last part to add eyes, a nose, a hat and a scarf.

**7** Ask an adult to bake your snowman in the oven at 180 °C (Gas Mark 4) until your snowman is dry, or leave it to dry naturally.

**8** When it has cooled down, you can paint your snowman white, and maybe even roll him in silver glitter. Try painting an orange nose, black eyes, a black            15
hat and a blue scarf. A coat of shiny varnish adds the finishing touch to your winter ornament.

**Top Tip!** If the dough is too wet it will be impossible to roll out, so add more flour and salt. If the dough is too dry it will break up, so add a little more water.

**1**   How many parts are used to make the body of the snowman?

_____

**2** What can you do if the dough is too wet?

1

_____

_____

**3** Why would you need an adult to bake the snowman?

1

_____

_____

**4** What is the purpose of baking the snowman?

1

_____

Use a line to join the following words to their word class as used in the text.

5

**5** in (line 12)                          adjective

**6** head (line 10)                      verb

**7** and (line 5)                         noun

**8** blue (line 16)                       conjunction

**9** mix (line 5)                         preposition

Total 9

# Test 23: **Missing Words**

These sentences have been jumbled up and all have **ONE** additional word. Select the extra word in each of the sentences by underlining **ONE** word from options **a–e**.

**4**

**Example:** so cream eat the were cakes delicious

       (The cream cakes were so delicious.)

**a** cakes    **b** the    **c** <u>eat</u>    **d** were    **e** cream

**1**   lamb birth to tiny a the elephant given ewe had

    **a** lamb    **b** birth    **c** elephant    **d** given    **e** ewe

**2**   forests in many the are United combined there Kingdom

    **a** forests    **b** many    **c** United    **d** combined    **e** Kingdom

**3**   food prepare we before hands our wash always we feet

    **a** food    **b** prepare    **c** before    **d** hands    **e** feet

**4**   Barry painted newspaper wrote local a the letter to

    **a** painted    **b** newspaper    **c** wrote    **d** local    **e** letter

Select the **TWO** odd words out on each line. Select your answers by underlining **TWO** of the options **a–e**.

**4**

**Example: a** friend    **b** companion    **c** <u>compact</u>    **d** <u>converted</u>    **e** buddy

**5**  **a** pretty    **b** cute    **c** monstrous    **d** beautiful    **e** ugly

**6**   **a** dive    **b** paddle    **c** sea    **d** water    **e** swim

**7**   **a** cheese    **b** milk    **c** yoghurt    **d** carrots    **e** potato

**8**   **a** nose    **b** eyes    **c** hearing    **d** smell    **e** sight

---

Choose **ONE** word that is the best fit in each of these sentences.
Underline your answer from options **a–e**.    6

**9**   Grandma _____ me for an overnight visit last weekend.

    **a** chose    **b** invited    **c** selected    **d** sent    **e** spent

**10**   After unpacking, I went downstairs and _____ her in the kitchen.

    **a** played    **b** ate    **c** found    **d** cooked    **e** looked

**11**   We made a milkshake using strawberries, milk and _____ cream.

    **a** rice    **b** custard    **c** carrots    **d** soup    **e** ice

**12**   Next we made fresh popcorn in a _____ on the stove.

    **a** basin    **b** jug    **c** kettle    **d** saucepan    **e** bowl

**13**   We then went into the television room to _____ the film.

    **a** watch    **b** sight    **c** perform    **d** know    **e** hear

**14**   I always have a fun time at Grandma's _____.

    **a** room    **b** caravan    **c** house    **d** village    **e** road

Total    14

# Test 24: **Mixed**

In each of the following words there are some letters missing. Complete each word by selecting the missing letters from options **a–e** to make a word that has a **SIMILAR** meaning to the word on the left.

 3

**1** action        m __ v __ m __ n __

   **a** o v e t     **b** o e e t     **c** o e e s     **d** o v e s     **e** a e e t

**2** crash        __ o __ l __ s __ o __

   **a** c l l a s     **b** c l a e n     **c** c r l t e     **d** c l i i n     **e** c l a i n

**3** animal        c __ e __ t __ r __

   **a** l a u e     **b** h e a h     **c** r a u e     **d** h a h s     **e** r e u e

Choose **ONE** word that is the best fit in each of these sentences. Underline your answer from options **a–e**.

 3

**4** The bonfire glowed with orange and yellow _____.

   **a** frames     **b** furnace     **c** flames     **d** plumes     **e** flumes

**5** The dark clouds in the sky made it look as if it might _____.

   **a** sunshine     **b** rain     **c** snow     **d** frost     **e** storm

**6** There are lots of _____ in our garden pond.

   **a** frogs     **b** snakes     **c** foxes     **d** hedgehogs     **e** water

Select the **TWO** odd words out on each line. Select your answers by underlining **TWO** of the options **a–e**.

4

7   **a** peas      **b** beans      **c** bread      **d** pasta      **e** sweetcorn

8   **a** panther      **b** rabbit      **c** tiger      **d** dog      **e** lion

9   **a** tent      **b** caravan      **c** holiday      **d** hotel      **e** vacation

10   **a** car      **b** van      **c** aeroplane      **d** bus      **e** helicopter

Select the **ONE** word on the right that has the most **OPPOSITE** meaning to the word on the left. Underline the correct answer.

5

11   left      **a** over      **b** right      **c** remain      **d** correct      **e** end

12   under      **a** below      **b** down      **c** over      **d** bottom      **e** top

13   break      **a** holiday      **b** destroy      **c** paste      **d** join      **e** crack

14   silence   **a** whisper      **b** shout      **c** noise      **d** peace      **e** night

15   climb      **a** fall      **b** ascend      **c** reach      **d** fetch      **e** mountain

Total    15

Read the following sentences and answer the questions with the most sensible word.

'We had a goose to guard our home, but I was scared of it!'

**1** What does the word 'guard' mean as used in the sentence?

   **a** guide    **b** protect    **c** pet    **d** see    **e** alarm

**2** What does the word 'scared' mean as used in the sentence?

   **a** amazed    **b** damaged    **c** horrified    **d** disliked    **e** nervous

'I drew the curtains as the light had gone.'

**3** What does the word 'drew' mean as used in the sentence?

   **a** sketched    **b** art    **c** pencilled    **d** closed    **e** opened

**4** What does the word 'gone' mean as used in the sentence?

   **a** come    **b** go    **c** travelled    **d** appeared    **e** disappeared

Select the **ONE** word on the right that has the most **SIMILAR** meaning to the word on the left. Underline the correct answer.

**5** divide     **a** multiply    **b** halve    **c** share    **d** subtract    **e** add

**6** sad     **a** happy    **b** cry    **c** smile    **d** upset    **e** confused

**7** watch     **a** know    **b** see    **c** tight    **d** turn    **e** time

Look at the words in the grid and then use them to answer the
questions that follow.

| a plain | b piece | c part | d illegal | e secret |
|---|---|---|---|---|
| f prefer | g mystery | h simple | i gently | j present |
| k return | l missed | m noisy | n softly | o above |
| p rein | q hear | r feel | s bury | t over |
| u weather | v touch | w lost | x here | y cover |

**8**  Find **TWO** words that are **OPPOSITE** to the word 'beneath'.

_____    _____

**9**  Find **TWO** words that are **OPPOSITE** to the word 'absent'.

_____    _____

**10**  Find **TWO** words that are **OPPOSITE** to the word 'decorated'.

_____    _____

**11**  Find **TWO** words that are most **SIMILAR** to the word 'lightly'.

_____    _____

**12**  Find **TWO** words that are most **SIMILAR** to the word 'hide'.

_____    _____

**13**  Find **TWO** words that are most **SIMILAR** to the word 'section'.

_____    _____

Total ___ 19

# Test 26: **Comprehension**

Read the text carefully and answer the questions that follow.

### The End of Mean Tom

Kind Tom used to be known as Mean Tom because he was a mean boy. He was the type of boy who kicked you when you walked past him. If he found a spider, he would throw it at the person most scared of spiders and if anyone had food, they would have to give it to Tom. The happiest days were the days when Tom was off school … that is,    **5** until Tom received a taste of his own medicine.

One Monday, Tom was being cruel, as usual. He had dared some of the boys to climb on the kitchen bins to look through the windows of the kitchens and to scare the dinner staff. Nobody liked to join in with any of Tom's dares, but everyone was too nervous to go against him.   **10** Tom jumped on the first bin and then pointed and laughed at one of the smaller boys who could not climb up. Tom was laughing hard as he jumped up and down on the bin until there was a loud 'BANG!' The bin fell over and Tom lost his footing, falling on the floor heavily. All of the contents of the bin tumbled out, covering Tom from top to toe.   **15** Fish scales, banana skins, potato peelings, cold baked beans – he was absolutely covered and he smelled terrible!

For the rest of the day, Tom had to sit in clothes from lost property, but his hair and his skin stank. Nobody wanted to stand anywhere near Tom and nobody would sit next to him either. Even the teachers   **20** avoided going anywhere near him. Tom very soon realised that it was horrible being laughed at. He vowed to change his ways and Mean Tom became known as Kind Tom.

**1**   Which **THREE** statements are true? Underline your answers.      3

   **a**   Tom would throw spiders at people who were scared of spiders.

   **b**   Tom would pinch food off people.

c   Tom would punch people as they walked past.

d   Tom liked to scare the dinner staff.

e   Tom never took time off school.

2   Why didn't anyone want to sit next to Tom?                                    1

a   They were scared of Tom.

b   The teachers were avoiding him.

c   Tom was being laughed at.

d   Tom smelled horrible.

e   Nobody wanted to sit down.

3   Why did Mean Tom become Kind Tom?                                             1

a   Tom hated being laughed at.

b   Tom was fed up with being mean.

c   Tom was told to be nicer.

d   Tom hated wearing clothes from lost property.

e   Tom ended up covered in fish scales and rotten food.

Use a line to join the following words to their word class as used in the text.      5

4   hair (line 19)                          conjunction

5   pointed (line 11)                       adjective

6   but (line 10)                           verb

7   cold (line 16)                          pronoun

8   he (line 1)                             noun

Total    10

# Test 27: **Missing Letters**

Find the missing four letters that need to be added to these words so that the sentence makes sense. The four letters do not have to make a word.

**4**

**Example:** I have great r_____m so I love to dance.

**a** ithe    **b** itit    **c** hyth    **d** hith    **e** itth

1   Snow White took a bite out of a poi_____us apple.

**a** suno    **b** sano    **c** sanu    **d** sunu    **e** sono

2   The tram conductor told eve_____e to sit down.

**a** ryon    **b** rvin    **c** rion    **d** rvon    **e** rywn

3   They dug a hole in the sand and found a tr_____re chest.

**a** esyu    **b** eshu    **c** easu    **d** essu    **e** eash

4   It was impo_____le to keep still while the music played.

**a** sibb    **b** siib    **c** ssib    **d** ssab    **e** sseb

In each of the following words there are some letters missing. Complete each word by selecting the missing letters from options **a–e** to make a word most **SIMILAR** in meaning to the word on the left.

**4**

**Example:** end          f __ n __ s __ (finish)

**a** i e s    **b** i s h    **c** e a t    **d** i i h    **e** a i t

5   say                    m __ n __ i __ n

**a** e t a    **b** e t u    **c** e t o    **d** e s o    **e** e s a

**6** inquire        __ u __ s __ i __ n

  **a** q a t a     **b** q e h a     **c** q e h o     **d** q e t a     **e** q e t o

**7** think        c __ n __ i __ e __

  **a** o t v r     **b** o t l s     **c** o s d r     **d** o s t r     **e** o s t s

**8** right        c __ r __ e __ t

  **a** o c r     **b** o r n     **c** o c n     **d** o r c     **e** u r n

---

Find the three-letter word that is needed to complete each word so that each sentence makes sense. The missing three letters must make a word.

**Example:** The boy pedalled his b_____cle up the hill.

  **a** act     **b** <u>icy</u>     **c** lay     **d** air     **e** ice

**9** We took a large box and basic_____y made a den.

  **a** age     **b** all     **c** and     **d** end     **e** ire

**10** My big brother is always di_____reeing with me.

  **a** rug     **b** rag     **c** tag     **d** tug     **e** sag

**11** I don't know whet_____ to take an umbrella with me.

  **a** her     **b** him     **c** his     **d** she     **e** hit

**12** The school trip to the science m_____um was so exciting.

  **a** awe     **b** ewe     **c** ooh     **d** use     **e** yew

Total   12

# Test 28: **Mixed**

Select the **ONE** word on the right that has the most **SIMILAR** meaning to the word on the left. Underline the correct answer.

**3**

**1**   medal     **a** ribbon    **b** mess    **c** boss    **d** award    **e** exam

**2**   scheme    **a** plan    **b** range    **c** big    **d** school    **e** mark

**3**   fare     **a** ground    **b** circus    **c** pale    **d** light    **e** cost

These sentences have been jumbled up and all have **ONE** additional word. Select the extra word in each of the sentences by underlining **ONE** word from options **a–e**.

**4**

**4**   rice curry our vegetable had we with apples

    **a** rice    **b** curry    **c** vegetable    **d** with    **e** apples

**5**   the tree blew the bricks wind off the leaves

    **a** tree    **b** blew    **c** bricks    **d** wind    **e** leaves

**6**   roses placed the stems vase in a scented Mum

    **a** placed    **b** vase    **c** scented    **d** stems    **e** Mum

**7**   goslings bird waddled the goose little by with her

    **a** goslings    **b** bird    **c** waddled    **d** little    **e** her

Select the **TWO** odd words out on each line. Select your answers by underlining **TWO** of the options **a–e**.

**8**  **a** rabbit  **b** camel  **c** fox  **d** elephant  **e** badger

**9**  **a** garage  **b** shed  **c** gate  **d** window  **e** door

**10**  **a** gallop  **b** nap  **c** sleep  **d** skip  **e** doze

Choose **ONE** word that is the best fit in each of these sentences. Underline your answer from the options **a–e**.

**11**  The soldiers _____ up the hill.

**a** slouched  **b** marched  **c** hopped  **d** pranced  **e** danced

**12**  Lots of rabbits sat _____ the grass in the fields.

**a** painting  **b** sipping  **c** drinking  **d** sucking  **e** nibbling

**13**  We laughed when we visited the _____ for the pantomime.

**a** ballet  **b** hospital  **c** cinema  **d** theatre  **e** shop

**14**  The cook _____ a wonderful cake.

**a** cut  **b** ingredients  **c** baked  **d** fried  **e** roasted

Total  14

# Test 29: **Mixed**

Look at the words in the grid and then use them to answer the questions that follow.

| **a** hot | **b** kind | **c** bad | **d** fine | **e** old |
|-----------|-----------|-----------|-----------|-----------|
| **f** type | **g** fresh | **h** dull | **i** cloudy | **j** kite |
| **k** stress | **l** shy | **m** title | **n** aged | **o** bell |
| **p** press | **q** rotten | **r** name | **s** wet | **t** ring |
| **u** new | **v** den | **w** heated | **x** core | **y** wise |

**1**  Find **TWO** words that are most **SIMILAR** to the word 'sort'.

_____     _____

**2**  Find **TWO** words that are most **SIMILAR** to the word 'grey'.

_____     _____

**3**  Find **TWO** words that are most **SIMILAR** to the word 'label'.

_____     _____

**4**  Find **TWO** words that are **OPPOSITE** to the word 'stale'.

_____     _____

**5**  Find **TWO** words that are **OPPOSITE** to the word 'cold'.

_____     _____

**6**  Find **TWO** words that are **OPPOSITE** to the word 'young'.

_____     _____

Read the following paragraph and add one word from the list to each space so that the paragraph makes sense. Each word used can only be used once.

| adults | born | newspapers | powerful | writer |

**7–11** Adrian Mitchell was _____ in London in 1932 and

became a well-loved _____. He adapted *The Lion,*

*the Witch and the Wardrobe* for the stage, wrote song lyrics, plays, a

novel and articles for _____, but it is his poetry for

both children and _____ that is so wonderful. His

writing is beautiful and always _____.

Select the **ONE** word on the right that has the most **OPPOSITE** meaning to the word on the left. Underline the correct answer.

**12** tired     **a** sleepy    **b** moody    **c** awake    **d** annoyed    **e** bed

**13** hungry    **a** food    **b** bored    **c** brave    **d** empty    **e** full

**14** cosy     **a** cold    **b** comfy    **c** room    **d** feeling    **e** warm

**15** smart    **a** hurt    **b** neat    **c** broad    **d** bright    **e** scruffy

Total   21

# Test 30: **Mixed**

Find the three-letter word that is needed to complete each word so
that each sentence makes sense. The missing three letters must make
a word.

**1**   Everyone who I am rel_____d to visited us for the party.

    **a** are     **b** art     **c** ate     **d** ear     **e** eat

**2**   I was so im_____ient, I could not wait for the food to arrive.

    **a** pat     **b** pet     **c** pit     **d** pot     **e** put

**3**   After_____ds we all danced to happy music.

    **a** why     **b** woe     **c** wed     **d** wad     **e** war

**4**   It was so pe_____ful and quiet in the garden.

    **a** are     **b** ear     **c** ail     **d** ace     **e** ark

**5**   We placed a tiny seed into each f_____erpot.

    **a** law     **b** low     **c** mew     **d** mow     **e** now

---

Select the **TWO** odd words out on each line. Select your answers by
underlining **TWO** of the options **a–e**.

**6**   **a** happy     **b** sad     **c** cheerful     **d** jolly     **e** miserable

**7**   **a** hair     **b** scratch     **c** skin     **d** scrub     **e** rub

8   **a** draw      **b** sketch      **c** pencil      **d** write      **e** pen

9   **a** football      **b** swimming      **c** cricket      **d** cycling      **e** netball

10   **a** break      **b** holiday      **c** snap      **d** crack      **e** weekend

---

The following sentences all have **ONE** word missing. Complete the sentences by selecting a word from options **a–e**.

( 5 )

11   It was hard to see very far because of the thick _____.

    **a** fog      **b** thunder      **c** sun      **d** light      **e** sky

12   We turned on the _____ and watched the programme.

    **a** radio      **b** television      **c** floor      **d** drums      **e** piano

13   The _____ moved unseen under the sea.

    **a** ship      **b** boat      **c** train      **d** submarine      **e** car

14   The teacher put a cross next to the _____ spellings.

    **a** many      **b** incorrect      **c** perfect      **d** all      **e** right

15   Moorhens swam _____ the lake like little balls of soot.

    **a** above      **b** across      **c** below      **d** beneath      **e** over

Total      15

# Test 31: **Mixed**

Look at the words in the grid and then use them to answer the questions that follow.

| | | | | |
|---|---|---|---|---|
| **a** main | **b** chap | **c** sale | **d** garage | **e** fair |
| **f** meet | **g** key | **h** stale | **i** dare | **j** flick |
| **k** mail | **l** soar | **m** season | **n** care | **o** flap |
| **p** mean | **q** pouch | **r** seat | **s** light | **t** fly |
| **u** man | **v** unkind | **w** sweet | **x** post | **y** flag |

**1**  Find **TWO** words that are **OPPOSITE** to the word 'caring'.

_____        _____

**2**  Find **TWO** words that are **OPPOSITE** to the word 'dark'.

_____        _____

**3**  Find **TWO** words that are **OPPOSITE** to the word 'unimportant'.

_____        _____

**4**  Find **TWO** words that are most **SIMILAR** to the word 'letters'.

_____        _____

**5**  Find **TWO** words that are most **SIMILAR** to the word 'glide'.

_____        _____

**6**  Find **TWO** words that are most **SIMILAR** to the word 'guy'.

_____        _____

Find the missing four letters that need to be added to these words so that the sentence makes sense. The four letters do not have to make a word.

**3**

**7** We changed p_____ion so that I could watch the film.

  **a** osst    **b** oshi    **c** osit    **d** osis    **e** ossi

**8** We needed injec_____s before we travelled abroad.

  **a** tion    **b** tean    **c** shun    **d** shen    **e** chen

**9** Gina ate e_____h at the Thanksgiving meal.

  **a** neag    **b** noup    **c** nugg    **d** nuff    **e** noug

These sentences have been jumbled up and all have **ONE** extra word. Underline the word that is not needed.

**3**

**10** club joined board the I school chess

**11** red colour is a scarlet shade of

**12** goat a hippopotamus milked we farm the at

Total    18

# Puzzle 1

# Hidden Animals

There are animals hidden in the two grids below. Find the first letter from the first column, the second letter from the second column, and so on. Each letter can only be used once. Write the animal names down in a list. The first one has been done as an example.

## Animals with 3-letter names

| d | i | w |
|---|---|---|
| p | **o** | t |
| f | o | x |
| c | a | **g** |
| h | o | t |
| c | e | g |
| r | a | n |

_____ *dog* _____

_____

_____

_____

_____

_____

_____

## Animals with 4-letter names

| d | o | r | n |
|---|---|---|---|
| g | **u** | a | r |
| h | i | **c** | e |
| b | a | a | **k** |
| d | i | s | r |
| l | e | e | t |
| f | e | o | h |

_____ *duck* _____

_____

_____

_____

_____

_____

_____

**Puzzle 2**

# Animal Letter Links

Take the last letter of the first animal to make the first letter of the next animal. The first link has been done as an example. See if you can make a chain longer than this one!

| 1st Link | 2nd Link | 3rd Link | 4th Link |
|---|---|---|---|
| hare | cat | gorilla | walrus |
| earwig | | | |
| gerbil | | | |
| lizard | | | |
| dalmatian | | | |
| newt | | | |
| tadpole | | | |

Why not try the same game but with different topics? Can you do boys' names, girls' names, food, games, colours or countries? The more that you play with words and letters, the wider your word knowledge will become.

## Puzzle 3

# Leap Frog

See if you can find the drinks hidden in the letter chains below. Starting from the first letter in the chain, jump over the next letter to collect the letter that is after it. Keep jumping until you reach the end. The first one has been done as an example.

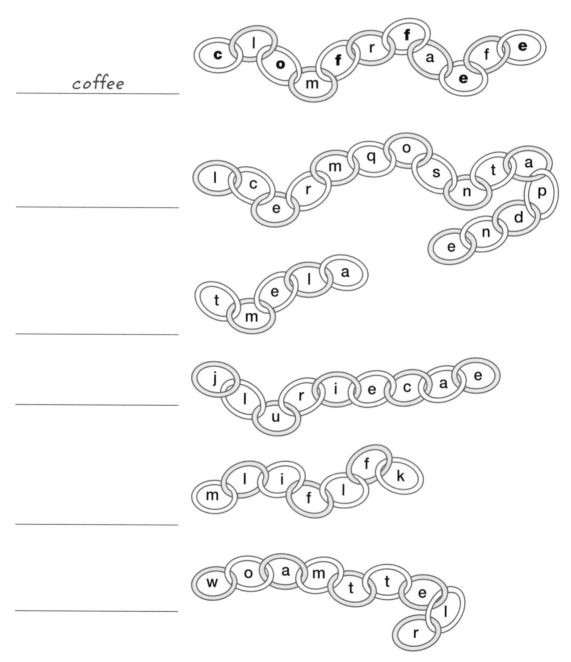

*coffee*

lemonade

tea

juice

milk

water

# Puzzle 4

## Fruit Spiral

There are 18 fruits hidden in this fruit spiral. Start on the first letter and then follow the spiral round, finding the 18 fruits as you go. The first has been done as an example.

| m | u | l | p | n | o | s | m | a | d |   |   |
|---|---|---|---|---|---|---|---|---|---|---|---|
| r |   |   |   |   |   |   |   |   |   |   |   |
| a | m | o | g | n | a | m | n | o | m | e | l |
| s | e |   |   |   |   |   |   |   |   |   | a |
| p | l |   | s | e | l | p | p | a | e |   | n |
| b | o |   | t |   |   |   |   | n |   |   | a |
| e | n |   | r |   | e | p | h |   | i |   | n |
| r | l |   | a |   | a |   | c |   | p |   | a |
| r | i |   | w |   | r |   | a |   | t |   | b |
| y | m |   | b |   |   |   | e |   | i |   | e |
| c | e |   | e | r | r | y | p |   | u |   | p |
| h | k |   |   |   |   |   |   |   | r |   | a |
| e | i | w | i | g | r | a | p | e | f |   | r |
| r |   |   |   |   |   |   |   |   |   |   | g |
| r | y | a | p | p | l | e | o | r | a | n | g | e |

___damson___  _____  _____

_____  _____  _____

_____  _____  _____

_____  _____  _____

_____  _____  _____

_____  _____  _____

**Puzzle 5**

# Word Search

Here are some words that describe noise. Can you find them in the grid?
One has been done for you.

| | | | | | |
|---|---|---|---|---|---|
| bang | ~~boom~~ | buzz | chatter | clap | clash |
| crack | crunch | fizz | giggle | hiss | patter |
| pop | rasp | ring | roar | scratch | sizzle |
| smash | stamp | thud | thump | tinkle | |

# Puzzle 6

## Missing Letters

The vegetables listed below have alternate letters missing. Can you fill in the gaps to reveal them? One has been done as an example. To help you, the missing letters are in the box on the right. You can cross them out once you've used them.

**Example:** s _w_ e _d_ e

1  c __ r __ o __

2  p __ r __ n __ p

3  c __ b __ a __ e

4  c __ u __ i __ l __ w __ r

5  s __ i __ a __ h

6  b __ o __ c __ l __

7  p __ t __ t __

8  s __ r __ u __ s

9  b __ a __ s

10  p __ a __

11  s __ e __ t __ o __ n

12  k __ l __

13  o __ i __ n

14  t __ r __ i __

15  c __ a __ d

16  l __ e __

17  c __ l __ r __

18  b __ e __ r __ o __

19  c __ u __ g __ t __ e

20  s __ e __ t    p __ t __ t __

a a a a a a a
b
c c c
e e e e e e e e e e
f
g
h
i i
k
l
n n n n
o o o o o o o o o o
p p p
r r r r r
s s
t t t t t
u
w w
y

# Puzzle 7

## Opposites

The word on the right is an opposite of the word on the left, but the letters have been jumbled up. When you have unscrambled them, write the word in the grid. The first letters of each word spell out another word. The first one has been done as an example.

| 1 | difficult | y a s e |
| 2 | fast | o w s l |
| 3 | teacher | l p i p u |
| 4 | start | d n e |
| 5 | dear | p e c h a |
| 6 | boiling | y i c |
| 7 | sleepy | k e w a a |
| 8 | first | s a l t |
| 9 | small | a g l e r |
| 10 | whisper | l e y l |

| e | a | s | y | |
|---|---|---|---|---|

What word is hidden in the grid? _____

# Sounds Like

A homophone is a word that sounds like another but has a different meaning and different spelling. Here are some words that are homophones. Write a homophone for each word next to it. Some of the words can have more than one homophone. One has been done as an example.

**Example:** banned ___*band*___

1. two _____

2. four _____

3. storey _____

4. hear _____

5. fare _____

6. yew _____

7. sew _____

8. wear _____

9. deer _____

10. nose _____

11. pear _____

12. week _____

# Progress chart

How did you do? Fill in your score below and shade in the corresponding boxes to compare your progress across the different tests.

50%     100%          50%     100%

**Test 1**, p2 Score: 10 /10

**Test 2**, p4 Score: 14 /14

**Test 3**, p6 Score: ____ /17

**Test 4**, p8 Score: ____ /12

**Test 5**, p10 Score: ____ /18

**Test 6**, p12 Score: ____ /14

**Test 7**, p14 Score: ____ /18

**Test 8**, p16 Score: ____ /20

**Test 9**, p18 Score: ____ /8

**Test 10**, p20 Score: ____ /15

**Test 11**, p22 Score: ____ /13

**Test 12**, p24 Score: ____ /10

**Test 13**, p26 Score: ____ /9

**Test 14**, p28 Score: ____ /18

**Test 15**, p30 Score: ____ /15

**Test 16**, p32 Score: ____ /13

**Test 17**, p34 Score: ____ /15

**Test 18**, p36 Score: ____ /13

**Test 19**, p46 Score: ____ /14

**Test 20**, p48 Score: ____ /14

**Test 21**, p50 Score: ____ /18

**Test 22**, p52 Score: ____ /9

**Test 23**, p54 Score: ____ /14

**Test 24**, p56 Score: ____ /15

**Test 25**, p58 Score: ____ /19

**Test 26**, p60 Score: ____ /10

**Test 27**, p62 Score: ____ /12

**Test 28** p64 Score: ____ /14

**Test 29**, p66 Score: ____ /21

**Test 30**, p68 Score: ____ /15

**Test 31**, p70 Score: ____ /18